Early
Phonics

snake

SCHOLASTIC

Published in the UK by Scholastic Education, 2020
Book End, Range Road, Witney, Oxfordshire, OX29 0YD

A division of Scholastic Limited
London – New York – Toronto – Sydney - Auckland
Mexico City – New Delhi – Hong Kong

www.scholastic.co.uk

1 2 3 4 5 6 7 8 9   0 1 2 3 4 5 6 7 8 9

British Library Cataloguing-in-Publication Data
A catalogue record for this book is available from the
British Library.

ISBN 978-1407-18356-5

Printed and bound by Ashford Colour Press
Papers used by Scholastic Limited are made from wood grown in
sustainable forests.

Author
Wendy Jolliffe

Editorial team
Rachel Morgan, Robin Hunt

Design team
Dipa Mistry, Andrea Lewis and Andrew Magee Design

Illustration
Carles Ballesteros

Contents

Phonics in the early years **4**

How to use this book **5**

Sound **s** **6**

Sound **a** **8**

Sound **t** **10**

Sound **p** **12**

Sound **i** **14**

Sound **n** **16**

Sound **e** **18**

Sound **d** **20**

Match the letters and pictures **22**

Match the words and pictures **23**

Silly sentences **24**

Writing practice **25**

Reading practice **26**

Mini-book: *Ned, Nat and ants* **27**

Certificate **32**

Phonics in the early years

This book will help your child to begin to learn about the sounds of our language, which form a vital building block for learning to read and spell. Try to ensure that these activities are kept short and are seen as fun, stopping as soon as your child is tired. Talking to your child as he or she does the activities is important too; hearing and saying the sounds is key to their understanding.

What is phonics?

Phonics refers to an approach that focuses on the sounds of our language and how these can be mapped to letters to help with reading and writing. All schools have a focus on phonics from Nursery onwards.

Children will learn phonics systematically when they start school, but you can help your child to make a good start by encouraging them to hear and identify individual sounds. It is important to make this fun. Some examples of games you can play include:

- **I hear with my little ear**: This is like the familiar game of 'I spy', except you hear the sound instead of looking for things that begin with a letter. For example, say: 'I hear with my little ear something beginning with "ffff"', placing emphasis on the sound.

Note that many sounds can be stretched, such as **m**, **s**, **f**, **l**, **r**, **n**, **v**, and **z**, for example 'mmm' or 'sss', which can help children in the beginning to identify individual sounds. Where you can't stretch the sound, as in **b**, try to avoid saying 'buh' and keep the 'uh' as short as possible, stressing the **b**.

- **Matching rhymes**: Here you can have fun saying words that rhyme, such as 'cat', 'hat', 'pat', 'rat', 'sat'. Rhyming is an important part of beginning to identify sounds. You may like to teach your child the well-known song 'There's a fox in a box in my little bed'. You'll find examples online, for instance:

> 'There's a fox in a box in my little bed, my little bed, my little bed.
> There's a fox in a box in my little bed and there isn't much room for me.'

Continue the song, making up further verses, such as 'There's a snake in a cake in my little bed...' or 'There's a giraffe in a scarf in my little bed...'.

Ensure all the emphasis on phonics is accompanied by lots of opportunities to share the wonderful world of children's books with your child, so that they see reading as a real pleasure.

How to use this book

In this book, you will find activities for each of the first sounds which form the start of most phonics programmes. These are **s, a, t, p, i, n, e, d**. These sounds can easily be made into short words, such as 'sat', 'hat', 'pin', 'dad', and so on. This is important as children need to learn to blend the sounds together to make words once they can hear and say the sounds correctly. In summary, the key for each sound is to:

- hear the sound (help your child to hear it correctly)
- say the sound (help your child to say the sound correctly)
- read the sound (help your child to read the sound correctly)
- write the sound (help your child to write the letter corresponding to the sound).

Try to do lots of oral activities that emphasise the first sound in a word. For example, when you are shopping, you might say 'some sssssoap', 'floppy ffffish'. Emphasise the first sound and say two or more words together that begin with the same sound.

This book provides two pages of activities for each of the first sounds. To help encourage your child, you will find a certificate on page 32 to display when they have completed all the activities.

Children can also colour or circle a face to show hard they found each activity.

Find a quiet space to look at the book with your child; preferably away from other distractions. Interacting is important, as is offering lots of praise for attempts.

 When appears, read the phrases and perform the actions. Emphasise the sounds in each phrase (e.g. **s**nakes on **s**lippery **s**and). Get your child to join in and repeat until they are confident with the sounds and the actions. A red 'Notes' box on each page also offers extra guidance for parents and carers working with their child.

On page 27 you will find the minibook *Ned, Nat and ants* for your child to practise reading the sounds he or she has learned. Reading a first book is a great achievement. Ensure you make it enjoyable, supporting your child and practising it so they can eventually learn to read it independently.

A copy of *Ned, Nat and ants* is also available online. You will also find instructions showing you how to make the printed pages into a minibook, a full set of answers and a copy of the certificate.
Visit www.scholastic.co.uk/flep35

Sound s

 Say the sound **s** and move your hand like a snake.

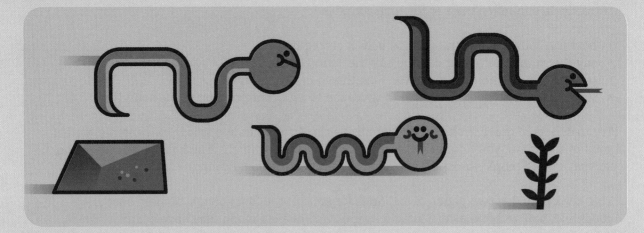

snakes on slippery sand

Colour the things that begin with the sound **s**.

Notes: Help your child to find the things that begin with the sound **s**. Say the word and emphasise the sound **s**.

Can you find six silly things beginning with **s**? Put a circle around the **s** words.

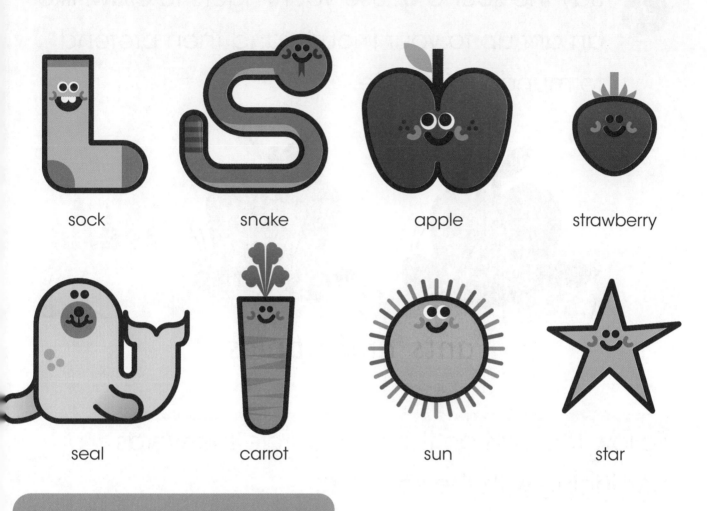

sock

snake

apple

strawberry

seal

carrot

sun

star

Write the letter **s** below.

S S S _____

Notes: Help your child to find and say the words that begin with the sound **s**. Have fun looking at the silly pictures.

How did you do?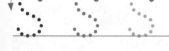

Sound a

Say the sound **a**. Use your fingers to crawl like an ant up to your mouth, and then pretend to munch an apple.

ants and apples

Follow the ants on their trail. Circle the words beginning with the sound **a**.

Notes: Help your child to find and say the words that begin with the sound **a**.

Say the **a** sound. Draw a <u>line</u> from the letter **a** to each picture that starts with that sound.

Write the letter **a**.

a a a

Notes: Help your child to find and say the words that begin with the sound **a**.

How did you do?

9

Sound t

 Stand on tiptoe and hold ten fingers up in the air. Say the sound **t**.

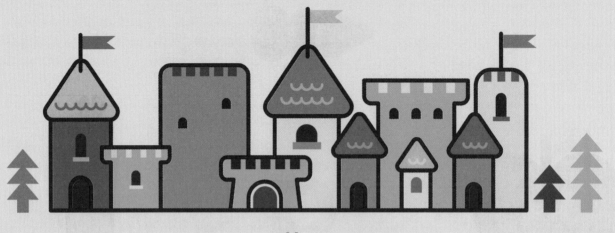

ten tall towers

Circle the words beginning with **t**.

Notes: Help your child to find and say the words that begin with the sound **t**. Draw lines to connect all the words that begin with **t**.

Tom is looking for a tiger. Circle the words beginning with the sound **t**.

Write the letter **t**.

t t t

Notes: Help your child to find and say the words that begin with the sound **t**.

How did you do?

11

Sound p

Say the sound **p** and pretend to stroke a pet.

pet in the park

Circle the animals that begin with the sound **p**.

Notes: Help your child to find and say the words that begin with the sound **p**. Have fun talking about which animals would make good pets.

Pop the balloons that have words that begin with the **p** sound. Cross out the balloons you pop.

Write the letter **p**.

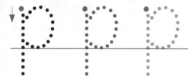

Notes: Help your child to find and say the words that begin with the sound **p**. Have fun saying you are popping the balloons – emphasising the **p** sound.

How did you do?

Sound i

 Say the sound **i** and jump up and down, pretending to scratch.

imps and itchy insects

Say the **i** sound. Draw a <u>line</u> from the letter **i** to the each picture that starts with that sound.

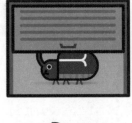

i

Notes: Help your child to find and say the words that begin with the sound **i**.

Find all the things beginning with **i** that are hiding in the snow. Put a circle around each one.

Write the letter **i**.

i i i

Notes: Help your child to find and say the words that begin with the sound **i**.

How did you do?

15

Sound n

 Pretend to throw a nut and catch it in a net.

nests and nets catch nuts

Catch the words that begin with **n** in the net.

Draw <u>lines</u> to join the **n** words to the net.

Notes: Help your child to find and say the words that begin with the sound **n**.

Circle the things in the next that begin with **n**.

Write the letter **n**.

n n n

Notes: Help your child to find and say the words that begin with the **n** sound.

How did you do?

17

Sound e

 Pretend to be an elephant with one arm dangling like a trunk.

elephants eat eleven eggs

Tick (✔) the eggs that have pictures that begin with **e**.

Notes: Help your child to find and say the words that begin with the **e** sound.

Look in the jungle. Can you spot the elephants?

Write the letter **e** on the things that begin with **e**.

Write the letter **e**.

Notes: Help your child to find and say the words that begin with the **e** sound. Help them to write the letter **e**, ensuring they begin at the correct starting point.

How did you do?

Sound d

 Pretend to dig, like a dog digging with its paws.

dogs and ducks dig dens

Can you help the animals find their dens? Draw a <u>line</u> from each animal beginning with **d** to a den.

Dens

Notes: Help your child to find and say the words that begin with the sound **d**.

Dig for dinosaurs and things that begin with **d**. (Circle) each item.

Write the letter **d**.

d   d   d

Notes: Help your child to find and say the words that begin with the sound **d**. Have fun saying you are digging for each object - emphasising the 'd' sound.

How did you do?

Match the letters and pictures

Draw <u>lines</u> to match the letters to the pictures.

n  i

 t  e

s  a

 p  d

Notes: Help your child to name each picture. Ask your child what letter each picture begins with, then match to the letters above.

How did you do?

Match the words and pictures

Draw lines to match each word to the correct picture.

ink

sandcastle

dinosaur

parrot

envelope

nut

turtle

ant

How did you do?

Silly sentences

Tell your helper when you hear a word that begins with **s**, **t** or **e**.

Silly snakes in the sand.

Tom sees ten tigers.

Seals sing in the sea.

Elephants eat eleven eggs.

Tom tickles ten turtles.

Echoes of elephants and elves.

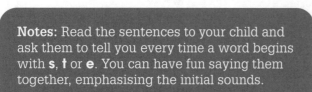

How did you do?

Writing practice

Reading practice

Read the words in the bubbles.

sat

pat

net

den

nit

pan

end

sit

ten

pen

Notes: Help your child to read the simple words in the bubbles, using the sounds they have learned. This will prepare them for reading the book *Ned, Nat and ants* on pages 27–31.

26

How did you do?

Words which the children will require support to read: **the**

Notes: Before you start please note that children will require support to read the word 'the' in this book. A mini-book version of these pages is also available online with instructions on how to put it together. Visit www.scholastic.co.uk/FLEP35

Ned, Nat and ants

Tap, tap, tap.

1

Tip, tap, tip, tap.

2

It's a din!

3

Ned and Nat sat in the tent.

4

An ant in the tent.

5

Ants in a tent!

6

Sad Ned and Nat!

7

8

★ ★ ★ ★ ★

Certificate

Well done!

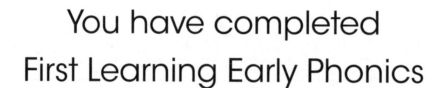

You have completed
First Learning Early Phonics

This certificate is awarded to:

....

Age: ....

★

Date: ....